DIALOGUE
with My
DAUGHTERS

MY PERSONAL REFLECTIONS

DIALOGUE
with My
DAUGHTERS

MY PERSONAL REFLECTIONS

JEFFREY A. JOHNSON, SR.

DIALOGUE WITH MY DAUGHTERS: MY PERSONAL REFLECTIONS
by Jeffrey A. Johnson, Sr.

Cover Design by Atinad Designs.

© Copyright 2011

SAINT PAUL PRESS, DALLAS, TEXAS

First Printing, 2011

The Bible quotations used in this volume are from the King James Version, the New International Version, and the New Living Translation.

The name SAINT PAUL PRESS and its logo are registered as a trademark in the U.S. patent office.

ISBN-10: 0-9838328-6-2
ISBN-13: 978-0-9838328-6-7

Printed in the U.S.A.

To Our Heavenly Father—
the Perfect Father,
the One who provides all of our needs,
the One who never rejects or abandons us,
the One who loves us just as we are.

"To our God and Father be glory for ever and ever.
Amen."

(PHILIPPIANS 4:20)

INTRODUCTION

My Daughter,

This journal is intended to give you the opportunity to reflect upon what you are reading in my book *Dialogue with My Daughters*. I want you to write down your own thoughts and feelings as you walk through each chapter. I've included some reflection ideas to guide you through this process, but these are only meant to help you to express what you think and what you feel. There are some extra pages at the end of each chapter so that you can write as much as you want in response to any of the reflections. Also, as something you read really goes deep within your spirit, capture your thoughts on paper. And write when you hear God speaking to you in a special way so that you remember what He is saying to you. Use this journal to write whatever you like, in whatever form you want. Pour your heart out and, as you do, know that God is listening and He cares.

This journal is between you and Him. Let it be part of your daily time with the Lord and allow God to speak to you even as you are opening your heart to Him. Know that I love you and that I have prayed for you—that God will:

open your eyes to see yourself the way He sees you,

open your mind to allow Him to free you
from all that hinders you,

open your hands to receive the blessings
He has for you, and

open your heart to experience
a transformation, a fresh start.

Be blessed, my daughter.

CHAPTER 1

Handle Your Beliefs

You Are Not Your Hair

For you created my inmost being;
> you knit me together in my mother's womb.

I praise you because I am fearfully and wonderfully made;
> your works are wonderful,
> I know that full well.

My frame was not hidden from you
> when I was made in the secret place,
> when I was woven together in the depths of
> the earth.

Your eyes saw my unformed body;
> all the days ordained for me were written
> in your book
> before one of them came to be.

How precious to me are your thoughts, God!
How vast is the sum of them!
Were I to count them,
> they would outnumber the grains of sand—
> when I awake, I am still with you.

PSALM 139:13-18

Dear Father,

I pray for my daughter as she reflects on the fact that she is not her hair. I pray that she will get a glimpse of herself as You see her. Show her all of the beauty that You see both within and without. Deliver her from a negative self-image. So often, when she looks into the mirror, she focuses only on something that isn't "right" about her appearance, and she never sees what You see. Father, help her to recognize that her initial impressions of herself—whether they were positive or negative—probably didn't come from You, but from someone else in her life. Let her know that she does not have to accept that person's opinion. Let her begin to look at herself afresh, through Your eyes. If there are things that she can change to make herself healthier, or to make herself feel better about her appearance, give her wisdom, inspiration, and direction to know how to go about doing that. Mostly, though, God, help her to focus on the inner person: who she is at the core of her being. Help her not to settle for being anyone less than the person You had in mind when You created her.

God, I can't be there to get rid of the monsters under her bed, or in her bed, or wherever they may be, but You can. Chase away her monsters, and give her peace. Replace her fear with confidence in You, and replace her sadness with the joy that comes from knowing You. Draw her close to You now and help her to know how much we both love her.

Amen.

DAUGHTER, REFLECT UPON...

What Psalm 139:13-18 means to you:

_____

_____

_____

_____

_____

_____

_____

_____

_____

What your mirror tells you when you look into it:

_____

_____

_____

_____

_____

_____

_____

_____

What you like about yourself:

_____

_____

_____

_____

_____

_____

_____

_____

_____

Where you think your attitudes toward yourself came from:

_____

_____

_____

_____

_____

_____

_____

_____

_____

_____

What you thought when you read the story of the young woman on *American Idol* who thought she was being judged because she was big:

_____

_____

_____

_____

_____

_____

_____

_____

_____

The world's definition of beauty:

_____

_____

_____

_____

_____

_____

_____

_____

_____

God's definition of beauty:

_____

_____

_____

_____

_____

_____

_____

_____

Your own definition of beauty:

_____

_____

_____

_____

_____

_____

_____

_____

_____

Whom you would consider "an ideal man," and why:

_____

_____

_____

_____

_____

_____

_____

_____

_____

One of the most hurtful things anybody ever said to you:

_____

_____

_____

_____

_____

_____

_____

_____

_____

How you wish you had handled that experience:

_____

_____

_____

_____

_____

_____

_____

_____

The monsters present in your life:

_____

_____

_____

_____

_____

_____

_____

_____

How you think you should handle them:

_____

_____

_____

_____

_____

_____

_____

_____

One of the kindest or most positive things anybody ever said to you:

_____

_____

_____

_____

_____

_____

_____

_____

What you wish your daddy had told you:

What you would say to your daddy, if you could talk heart-to-heart with him and tell him anything:

Things you want to do to become a healthier you:

_____

_____

_____

_____

_____

_____

_____

_____

_____

Your Prayer to God:

_____

_____

_____

_____

_____

_____

_____

_____

_____

_____

_____

_____

_____

_____

_____

_____

_____

_____

_____

_____

_____

_____

ADDITIONAL THOUGHTS:

_____
_____
_____
_____
_____
_____
_____
_____
_____
_____
_____
_____
_____
_____
_____
_____
_____
_____
_____
_____
_____
_____

CHAPTER 2

Handle Your Body

Keep Your Cookies in the Cookie Jar

You say, "I am allowed to do anything"—but not everything is good for you. And even though "I am allowed to do anything," I must not become a slave to anything. You say, "Food was made for the stomach, and the stomach for food." (This is true, though someday God will do away with both of them.) But you can't say that our bodies were made for sexual immorality. They were made for the Lord, and the Lord cares about our bodies. And God will raise us from the dead by his power, just as he raised our Lord from the dead. Don't you realize that your bodies are actually parts of Christ? Should a man take his body, which is part of Christ, and join it to a prostitute? Never! And don't you realize that if a man joins himself to a prostitute, he becomes one body with her? For the Scriptures say, "The two are united into one." But the person who is joined to the Lord is one spirit with him. Run from sexual sin! No other sin so clearly affects the body as this one does. For sexual immorality is a sin against your own body. Don't you realize that your body is the temple of the Holy Spirit, who lives in you and was given to you by God? You do not belong to yourself, for God bought you with a high price. So you must honor God with your body.

(1 Corinthians 6:12-20, NLT)

DEAR GOD,

You know how priceless my daughter is. You know how many boys and men there are in the world who do not appreciate girls and women as they should. They do not recognize their infinite value, nor do they recognize who their Father is. I pray, God, that you will protect my daughter, Your daughter. Help her to make wise decisions: to choose her friends well; to run from any boy or man who tries to take from her what is intended for her to give someday to her husband; to remember that her body is the temple of the Holy Spirit and to treat it with dignity and respect; to shun any person who does not also treat her with dignity and respect; and to remember always that she is fearfully and wonderfully made.

Give her patience, Lord, and help her to remember that Your timing is perfect. Remind her also that she is not her own. You bought her with a price and she belongs to You. In Your own timing, God, bless her with a loving husband who recognizes her value and treats her as a daughter of the King. And help her always to remember who she is and Whose she is.

Amen.

Daughter, reflect upon...

What 1 Corinthians 6:12-20 means to you:

_____

_____

_____

_____

_____

_____

_____

_____

_____

Any "cookie monsters" you have known or known about, and how they behaved:

_____

_____

_____

_____

_____

_____

_____

_____

How you want to be treated by men who are interested in you:

_____

_____

_____

_____

_____

_____

_____

_____

Why it's important to wait until marriage before having sex:

_____

_____

_____

_____

_____

_____

_____

_____

What questions you have about sex, and the knowledgeable, understanding person(s) you can go to for correct answers:

_____

_____

_____

_____

_____

_____

_____

_____

_____

What your boundaries are, and what they say about you:

_____

_____

_____

_____

_____

_____

_____

_____

_____

Some of the things that tempt you, or that make you feel vulnerable:

_____

_____

_____

_____

_____

_____

_____

_____

Things you can do to avoid yielding to temptation:

_____

_____

_____

_____

_____

_____

_____

_____

The qualities you want in a husband:

_____
_____
_____
_____
_____
_____
_____
_____

Your dream wedding:

_____
_____
_____
_____
_____
_____
_____
_____

The TV shows and movies that have influenced your views about love, sex and marriage:

_____

_____

_____

_____

_____

_____

_____

_____

The prayer that David prayed in Psalm 51:1-4, 10-17:

_____

_____

_____

_____

_____

_____

_____

_____

How you feel knowing that sex is a gift from God:

_____

_____

_____

_____

_____

_____

_____

_____

What you envision your marriage looking like/how you will be as a couple:

_____

_____

_____

_____

_____

_____

_____

_____

Your prayer to God:

_____

_____

_____

_____

_____

_____

_____

_____

_____

_____

_____

_____

_____

_____

_____

_____

_____

_____

_____

_____

ADDITIONAL THOUGHTS:

CHAPTER 3

Handle Your Brain

Free Your Mind and the Rest Will Follow

Do not conform to the pattern of this world, but be transformed by the renewing of your mind. Then you will be able to test and approve what God's will is—his good, pleasing and perfect will.

(ROMANS 12:2)

God,

You know the pull of this world on the lives of Christian girls and women. The enemy wants nothing more than to get my daughter's mind so bound, so captivated by something in this world that she no longer seeks You or Your will for her life. As much as she loves You and wants to please You, she is still human and still vulnerable. And the enemy is so deceptive. The enemy can take even something that is potentially good and use it to get her sidetracked.

I pray for her, Lord God, that You will deliver her from the evil one. I pray that You will give her the strength and grace to continually renew her mind so that she can be transformed into the likeness of Jesus. Give her a taste for eternal things and for the things of Your kingdom, so that she is not satisfied with anything this world has to offer. Free her mind, Lord, so that she can follow you wholly and so that she can experience Your good, pleasing and perfect will in her life.

Amen.

DAUGHTER, REFLECT UPON...

What Romans 12:2 means to you:

_____

_____

_____

_____

_____

_____

_____

_____

A time when you were tempted to believe something different from what God's Word says:

_____

_____

_____

_____

_____

_____

_____

_____

What it means when we say, "heart follows head":

_____

_____

_____

_____

_____

_____

_____

_____

How much (or little) you trust your Heavenly Father to do what is good for you:

_____

_____

_____

_____

_____

_____

_____

_____

_____

Some specific things that express "the lust of the flesh, the lust of the eyes, and the pride of life":

_____

_____

_____

_____

_____

_____

_____

_____

_____

Whether you feel you currently are fitting in more with the world or with God's kingdom:

_____

_____

_____

_____

_____

_____

_____

_____

_____

What the pressures are on you to choose to please the world more than God:

_____

_____

_____

_____

_____

_____

_____

_____

How much you are influenced by what you see on TV, or in movies, or magazines:

_____

_____

_____

_____

_____

_____

_____

_____

The area(s) you want to work on in your life to line them up with the Word of God:

_____

_____

_____

_____

_____

_____

_____

_____

_____

What specific things you can do to strengthen your efforts to change:

_____

_____

_____

_____

_____

_____

_____

_____

What "transformation"/"metamorphosis" looks like to you—what you will look like when you are transformed:

_____

_____

_____

_____

_____

_____

_____

_____

_____

A time when you believed someone else instead of God, and what happened:

_____

_____

_____

_____

_____

_____

_____

_____

_____

All of those who currently influence your mind/your thinking:

_____

_____

_____

_____

_____

_____

_____

_____

_____

What you don't know now that you want to know for the future:

_____

_____

_____

_____

_____

_____

_____

_____

_____

What a negative person looks like and whether or not you believe yourself to be that way:

_____

_____

_____

_____

_____

_____

_____

_____

_____

The last pity party you threw for yourself and the outcome:

_____

_____

_____

_____

_____

_____

_____

_____

_____

What you can do to avoid the temptation of throwing a pity party:

_____

_____

_____

_____

_____

_____

_____

_____

_____

How honoring someone else can bring honor to yourself:

_____

_____

_____

_____

_____

_____

_____

_____

_____

Whether or not you have a healthy work ethic:

_____

_____

_____

_____

_____

_____

_____

_____

_____

The most difficult challenge you have had in forgiving someone, and how you are doing:

_____

_____

_____

_____

_____

_____

_____

_____

_____

The negative consequences of harboring a victim mentality:

_____

_____

_____

_____

_____

_____

_____

_____

_____

Some principles of God that you want to want to keep in mind:

_____

_____

_____

_____

_____

_____

_____

_____

_____

YOUR PRAYER TO GOD:

_____

_____

_____

_____

_____

_____

_____

_____

_____

_____

_____

_____

_____

_____

_____

_____

_____

_____

_____

_____

_____

ADDITIONAL THOUGHTS:

CHAPTER 4

Handle Your Business

Girl, Get Your Money Straight

Who can find a virtuous woman? for her price is far above rubies.

The heart of her husband doth safely trust in her, so that he shall have no need of spoil.

She will do him good and not evil all the days of her life.

She seeketh wool, and flax, and worketh willingly with her hands.

She is like the merchants' ships; she bringeth her food from afar.

She riseth also while it is yet night, and giveth meat to her household, and a portion to her maidens.

She considereth a field, and buyeth it: with the fruit of her hands she planteth a vineyard.

She girdeth her loins with strength, and strengtheneth her arms.

She perceiveth that her merchandise is good: her candle goeth not out by night.

She layeth her hands to the spindle, and her hands hold the distaff.

She stretcheth out her hand to the poor; yea, she reacheth forth her hands to the needy.

She is not afraid of the snow for her household: for all her household are clothed with scarlet.

She maketh herself coverings of tapestry; her clothing is silk and purple.

Her husband is known in the gates, when he sitteth among the elders of the land.

She maketh fine linen, and selleth it; and delivereth girdles unto the merchant.

Strength and honour are her clothing; and she shall rejoice in time to come.

She openeth her mouth with wisdom; and in her tongue is the law of kindness.

She looketh well to the ways of her household, and eateth not the bread of idleness.

Her children arise up, and call her blessed; her husband also, and he praiseth her.

Many daughters have done virtuously, but thou excellest them all.

Favour is deceitful, and beauty is vain: but a woman that feareth the LORD, she shall be praised.

Give her of the fruit of her hands; and let her own works praise her in the gates.

(PROVERBS 31:10-31, KJV)

Heavenly Father,

When I think of my daughter, I long for her to become a Proverbs 31 woman. I believe that woman was filled with joy and contentment because she was living her life in a way that pleased You, and in a way that cared for others. Her life was meaningful. She had purpose. Every morning when she woke up, she knew that she was going to accomplish something of significance. She wasn't afraid of hard work, but her work was to gain things of lasting value, not the temporal things that would slip through her fingers and keep her constantly wanting more.

God, I want my daughter to know that life of meaning and purpose. I want her to be happy. I want her to experience that moment when her children rise up and call her blessed, and her husband praises her to his friends. I want her to know the sense of fulfillment of having her community, those whose lives she touches, acknowledge the value she adds to their lives. O God, my daughter is so full of potential and has such wonderful gifts and talents. Please guide her step by step as she continues to develop her relationship with You and with others. Help her to get her money straight so that she can be blessed, and be a blessing, throughout her life. Make her wealthy in all the things that are important and lasting.

Amen.

Daughter, reflect upon...

What Proverbs 31:10-31 means to you:

_____

_____

_____

_____

_____

_____

_____

_____

_____

_____

Something that you want, even long for, but do not have:

_____

_____

_____

_____

_____

_____

_____

_____

_____

_____

The fact that you *are* somebody; you *are* priceless:

_____

_____

_____

_____

_____

_____

_____

_____

Whether you are a producer or a consumer; think of examples:

_____

_____

_____

_____

_____

_____

_____

_____

_____

How you spend your money and where the greatest percentage of it goes:

_____

_____

_____

_____

_____

_____

_____

_____

_____

A time or times that you expected compliments merely for being a consumer:

_____

_____

_____

_____

_____

_____

_____

_____

_____

Things you've learned along the way that have made a significant difference in your life:

_____

_____

_____

_____

_____

_____

_____

_____

Something you need to learn in order to fulfill your God-planned destiny:

_____

_____

_____

_____

_____

_____

_____

_____

Your own ability (or inability) to delay gratification in order to attain a greater goal:

_____

_____

_____

_____

_____

_____

_____

_____

_____

Something you purchased, but wished later you hadn't, and what you learned from that:

_____

_____

_____

_____

_____

_____

_____

_____

_____

The difference between money and wealth:

_____

_____

_____

_____

_____

_____

_____

_____

A lesson you learned from some game that *you* played:

_____

_____

_____

_____

_____

_____

_____

_____

_____

The blessings of tithing, giving offerings, and sharing with the poor:

_____

_____

_____

_____

_____

_____

_____

_____

Anything that happened in your past that has become a psychological barrier for you:

_____

_____

_____

_____

_____

_____

_____

_____

Whether or not you have a victim mentality:

_____

_____

_____

_____

_____

_____

_____

_____

_____

A decision you have made, or need to make, to propel your life forward:

_____

_____

_____

_____

_____

_____

_____

_____

_____

One of your character traits that is worthy of praise:

_____

_____

_____

_____

_____

_____

_____

_____

_____

YOUR PRAYER TO GOD:

_____

_____

_____

_____

_____

_____

_____

_____

_____

_____

_____

_____

_____

_____

_____

_____

_____

_____

_____

_____

_____

_____

ADDITIONAL THOUGHTS:

CHAPTER 5

Handle Your Blessings

Do You

When the queen of Sheba heard about the fame of Solomon and his relationship to the LORD, she came to test Solomon with hard questions. Arriving at Jerusalem with a very great caravan—with camels carrying spices, large quantities of gold, and precious stones—she came to Solomon and talked with him about all that she had on her mind. Solomon answered all her questions; nothing was too hard for the king to explain to her. When the queen of Sheba saw all the wisdom of Solomon and the palace he had built, the food on his table, the seating of his officials, the attending servants in their robes, his cupbearers, and the burnt offerings he made at the temple of the LORD, she was overwhelmed. She said to the king, "The report I heard in my own country about your achievements and your wisdom is true. But I did not believe these things until I came and saw with my own eyes. Indeed, not even half was told me; in wisdom and wealth you have far exceeded the report I heard."

(1 KINGS 10:1-7)

LORD GOD,

Please help my daughter to see herself as part of a royal family. Help her to recognize her queenly potential and to live her life accordingly. Inspire her to seek relationships with those who are also living for You. Give her the humility to seek wisdom from those who are wise, and understanding from those who know You intimately.

God, spare my daughter from ever trying to be like anyone else but Jesus. Let her never become an imperfect copy of someone else, but rather let her find joy in discovering the precious original you created her to be. Give her life experiences beyond all that she could ever dream. Give her a spirit of adventure so that she will never be afraid to follow You. Bless her, Lord, I pray.

Amen.

Daughter, reflect upon...

What 1 Kings 10:1-7 means to you:

_____

_____

_____

_____

_____

_____

_____

_____

_____

What you can do to become the woman your prince will want to marry:

_____

_____

_____

_____

_____

_____

_____

_____

_____

_____

What you can do to become the woman Your Father
wants you to be:

_____

_____

_____

_____

_____

_____

_____

_____

A vision of what the best you possible would look like:

_____

_____

_____

_____

_____

_____

_____

_____

The *type* of man you would like someday to marry:

_____

_____

_____

_____

_____

_____

_____

_____

_____

Qualities of the Proverbs 31 woman that you want to cultivate in your life:

_____

_____

_____

_____

_____

_____

_____

_____

_____

The concerns related to online dating services:

_____

_____

_____

_____

_____

_____

_____

_____

Those within your support system and why you know you can trust them:

_____

_____

_____

_____

_____

_____

_____

_____

_____

Male friends you have had who have blessed your life just by their friendship:

_____

_____

_____

_____

_____

_____

_____

_____

_____

Key qualities you have seen and appreciated in your male friends:

_____

_____

_____

_____

_____

_____

_____

_____

_____

Ways you can get to know a person better:

_____

_____

_____

_____

_____

_____

_____

_____

Discovering a man's priorities by the way he spends his money:

_____

_____

_____

_____

_____

_____

_____

_____

_____

Fairy tale expectations you must give up to find your prince:

_____

_____

_____

_____

_____

_____

_____

_____

YOUR PRAYER TO GOD:

_____

_____

_____

_____

_____

_____

_____

_____

_____

_____

_____

_____

_____

_____

_____

_____

_____

_____

_____

ADDITIONAL THOUGHTS:

_____

_____

_____

_____

_____

_____

_____

_____

_____

_____

_____

_____

_____

_____

_____

_____

_____

_____

CHAPTER 6

Handle Your Basics

Put a Ring on It

At that time the kingdom of heaven will be like ten virgins who took their lamps and went out to meet the bridegroom. Five of them were foolish and five were wise. The foolish ones took their lamps but did not take any oil with them. The wise ones, however, took oil in jars along with their lamps. The bridegroom was a long time in coming, and they all became drowsy and fell asleep.

At midnight the cry rang out: 'Here's the bridegroom! Come out to meet him!'

Then all the virgins woke up and trimmed their lamps. The foolish ones said to the wise, 'Give us some of your oil; our lamps are going out.'

'No,' they replied, 'there may not be enough for both us and you. Instead, go to those who sell oil and buy some for yourselves.'

But while they were on their way to buy the oil, the bridegroom arrived. The virgins who were ready went in with him to the wedding banquet. And the door was shut.

Later the others also came. 'Lord, Lord,' they said, 'open the door for us!' But he replied, 'Truly I tell you, I don't know you.'

Therefore keep watch, because you do not know the day or the hour.

(MATTHEW 25:1-13)

DEAR FATHER,

As we come to the close of this book and journal, I pray that you will speak deeply to our daughter. May Your priorities become her priorities. May Your thoughts become her thoughts. May Your desires for her become her desires.

Prepare her for the days ahead—both in this life and the life to come. Help her to know that she is loved, and remind her that she never walks alone.

Amen.

DAUGHTER, REFLECT UPON...

What Matthew 25:1-13 means to you:

_____

_____

_____

_____

_____

_____

_____

_____

_____

The circumstances that should be in order before a couple marry:

_____

_____

_____

_____

_____

_____

_____

_____

_____

The importance of being able to care for yourself without a man:

_____

_____

_____

_____

_____

_____

_____

_____

The female friends in your life, and whether they are positive or negative influences:

_____

_____

_____

_____

_____

_____

_____

_____

The qualities you want your closest female friends to have:

_____

_____

_____

_____

_____

_____

_____

_____

_____

The "just enough" mentality:

_____

_____

_____

_____

_____

_____

_____

_____

_____

Changes you might want to make so you will be recognized for your queenly potential:

_____

_____

_____

_____

_____

_____

_____

_____

How a woman can help to make her marriage better:

_____

_____

_____

_____

_____

_____

_____

_____

The fact that God wants the best for you:

_____

_____

_____

_____

_____

_____

_____

_____

Anyone from the past that you need to let go of in order to make room for the future:

_____

_____

_____

_____

_____

_____

_____

_____

_____

Your response to Ephesians 5: 21-33:

_____

_____

_____

_____

_____

_____

_____

_____

_____

How you envision your home life:

_____

_____

_____

_____

_____

_____

_____

_____

_____

What you can do to make Jesus feel more comfortable in your home:

_____

_____

_____

_____

_____

_____

_____

_____

_____

The second chances God has already given you…and the third…and the fourth…:

_____

_____

_____

_____

_____

_____

_____

_____

_____

Your hope for your future:

_____

_____

_____

_____

_____

_____

_____

_____

_____

YOUR PRAYER TO GOD:

_____

_____

_____

_____

_____

_____

_____

_____

_____

_____

_____

_____

_____

_____

_____

_____

_____

_____

_____

_____

ADDITIONAL THOUGHTS: